The Boosey & Hawkes
Solo Piano
Collection

RUSSIAN MASTERS

26 Russian classics arranged for
the intermediate pianist

selected by Hywel Davies

BOOSEY & HAWKES

Boosey & Hawkes Music Publishers Ltd
www.boosey.com

Published by Boosey & Hawkes Music Publishers Ltd
Aldwych House
71–91 Aldwych
London
WC2B 4HN

www.boosey.com

ISMN 979-0-060-12387-0
ISBN 978-0-85162-652-9

Third impression 2020

Printed by Halstan:
Halstan UK, 2–10 Plantation Road, Amersham, Bucks, HP6 6HJ. United Kingdom
Halstan DE, Weißliliengasse 4, 55116 Mainz. Germany

Music origination by Robin Hagues
Cover design by Fresh Lemon

CONTENTS

HYWEL DAVIES

Hywel Davies was born and brought up in London. He is active as a creative artist, editor and arranger. An award-winning composer, he has a long-standing association with Kokoro (Bournemouth Symphony Orchestra's new music ensemble) and other musicians and ensembles across Europe and North America; he was also the recipient of an Arts Council England International Fellowship in 2003. As a sonic artist and installation artist he has made works for Arts Council England's internal phone system, the former USAF base at Greenham Common and a ringtone to mark the handover of the Olympic flag from Beijing to London. His work as an arranger has been published by Boosey & Hawkes, Durand-Salabert-Eschig, Chester Music, Novello, the Associated Board of the Royal Schools of Music and Music Sales. For Boosey & Hawkes his arrangements have included two volumes of pieces by Astor Piazzolla and a volume of works by Rachmaninoff; he has also compiled four anthologies of piano music for them — *Animations, Contemplations, Fascinations* and *Gradations*. His work as a music editor began in 1988 when he joined Chester Music as Nicholas Hare's assistant.

www.hyweldavies.co.uk

NICHOLAS HARE

Nicholas Hare was born in 1940 and was a chorister at St George's Chapel, Windsor, under Dr William Harris. In 1954 he won a music scholarship to Marlborough College, Wiltshire, where he studied piano, organ and violin, and in 1959 was awarded a scholarship to Corpus Christi College, Oxford where he studied with Dr Sydney Watson. For ten years Nicholas served as Assistant Director and then Director of Music at Cheltenham College Junior, where he gained experience working with choirs and orchestras. During this period he also directed Music Vera chamber choir in Cheltenham. In 1979 he joined the editorial department of Chester Music working on a variety of educational projects and classical publications, including the preparation of new material for many premieres. Since 1990 Nicholas has worked as a freelance editor and arranger for Boosey & Hawkes, Chester Music, Faber Music, Trinity College London, the Associated Board of the Royal Schools of Music and others.

www.haremusic.co.uk

CHRISTOPHER NORTON

Christopher Norton was born in New Zealand in 1953. After graduating he began his career as a teacher, pianist and composer, and began to develop an interest in popular music. Coming to the UK in 1977 on a university scholarship, he studied composition at York University with Wilfred Mellers and David Blake. He is now well established as a composer, producer, arranger and educationalist and has written stage musicals, ballet scores, piano music, popular songs and orchestral music as well as jingles and signature tunes for TV and radio. He has lectured all over the world on aspects of his work and likes to integrate traditional teaching methods with aspects of modern technology. Chris is best known for his world-famous series *Microjazz* — easy graded pieces in modern styles such as blues, rock 'n' roll, reggae and jazz — and for his award-winning *Essential Guides to Pop Styles, Latin Styles* and *Jazz Styles*.

www.christophernorton.com

PRINCE IGOR
Polovtsian dance

ALEXANDER BORODIN
(1833–1887)
arranged by Hywel Davies

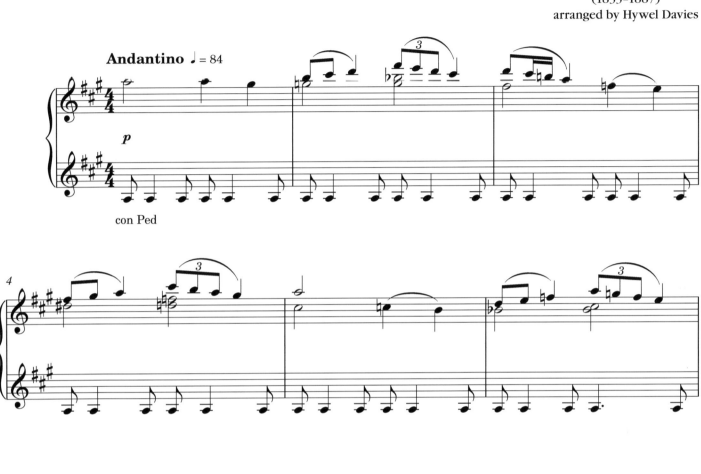

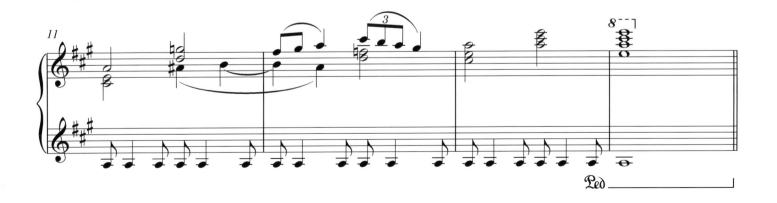

2

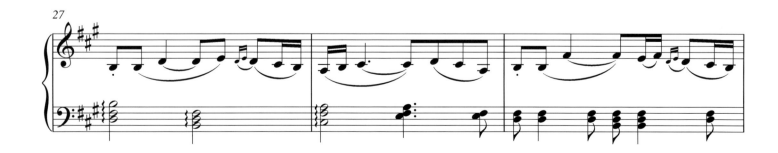

STRING QUARTET No 2
Nocturne

ALEXANDER BORODIN
(1833–1887)
arranged by Hywel Davies

RUSSLAN AND LUDMILLA
Overture

MIKHAIL GLINKA
(1804–1857)
arranged by Hywel Davies

PIANO CONCERTO No 3
Theme from second movement

DMITRY KABALEVSKY
(1904–1987)
arranged by Hywel Davies

MASQUERADE
Waltz

ARAM KHACHATURIAN
(1903–1978)
arranged by Hywel Davies

SPARTACUS
Adagio of Spartacus and Phrygia

ARAM KHACHATURIAN
(1903–1978)
arranged by Hywel Davies

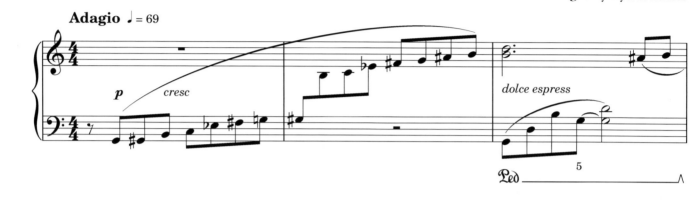

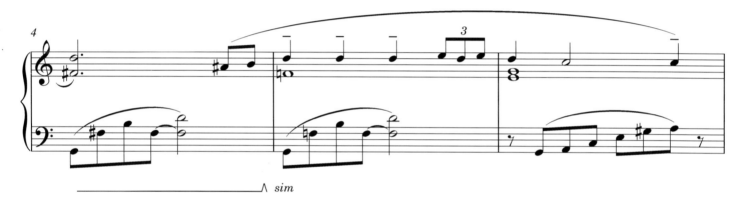

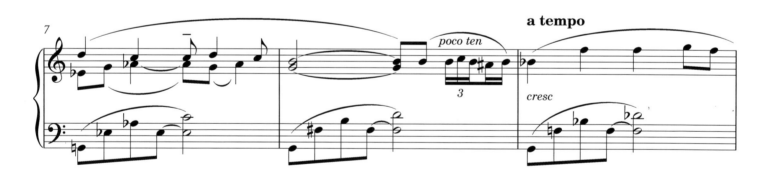

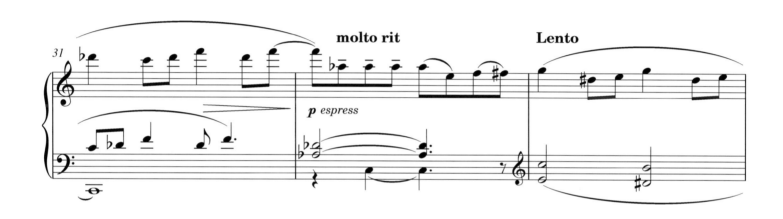

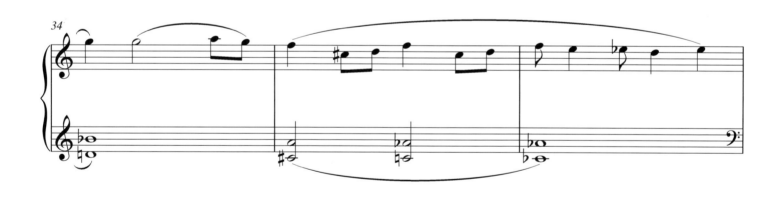

GAYANEH
Sabre dance

ARAM KHACHATURIAN
(1903–1978)
arranged by Christopher Norton

PICTURES AT AN EXHIBITION
Promenade

MODESTE MOUSSORGSKY
(1839–1881)
arranged by Hywel Davies

Allegro giusto, nel modo russico; senza allegrezza, ma poco sostenuto

CINDERELLA
Cinderella's waltz

SERGE PROKOFIEFF
(1891–1953)
arranged by Hywel Davies

Allegro espressivo ♩. = 50

poco rit

a tempo

PETER AND THE WOLF
Peter's theme

SERGE PROKOFIEFF
(1891–1953)
arranged by Christopher Norton

Andantino ♩ = 92

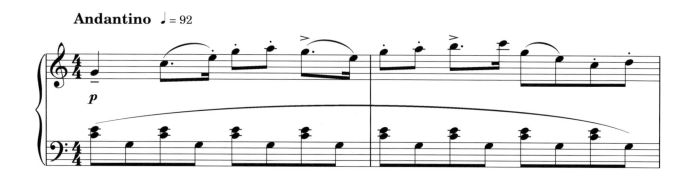

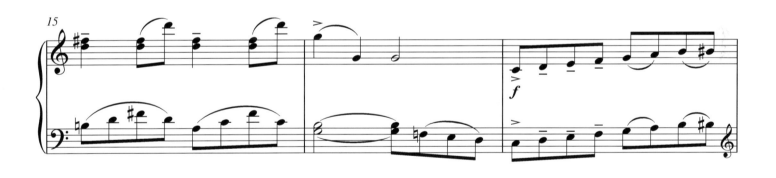

The Cat

arranged by Hywel Davies

Hunter's theme

arranged by Christopher Norton

Allegro moderato ♩ = 116

LIEUTENANT KIJÉ
Troika

SERGE PROKOFIEFF
(1891–1953)
arranged by Christopher Norton

Allegro con brio ♩ = 152

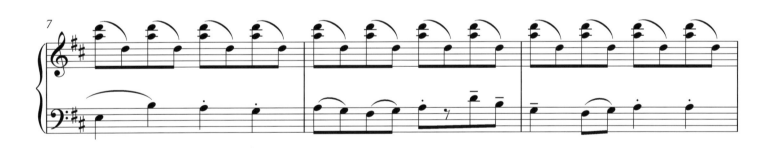

ROMEO AND JULIET
Montagues and Capulets

SERGE PROKOFIEFF
(1891–1953)
arranged by Hywel Davies
and Christopher Norton

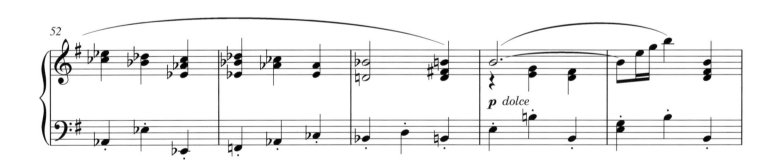

VOCALISE

SERGEI RACHMANINOFF
(1873–1943)
arranged by Nicholas Hare

★Small notes 2nd time only

RHAPSODY ON A THEME OF PAGANINI
18th variation

SERGEI RACHMANINOFF
(1873-1943)
arranged by Hywel Davies

PIANO CONCERTO No 2
Theme from second movement

SERGEI RACHMANINOFF
(1873–1943)
arranged by Hywel Davies

un poco più animato

SYMPHONY No 2
Theme from second movement

SERGEI RACHMANINOFF
(1873–1943)
arranged by Nicholas Hare

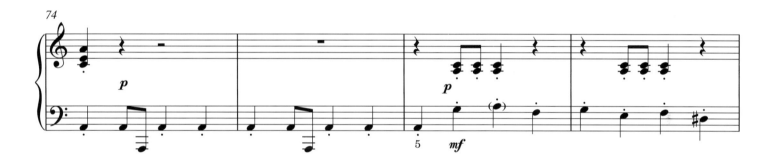

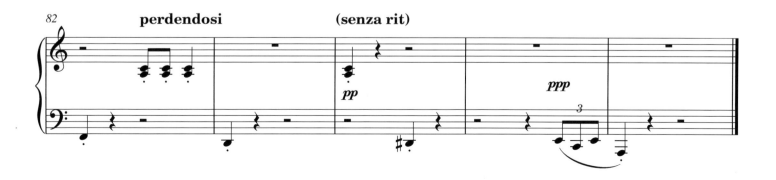

SHEHERAZADE
The young prince and the young princess

NIKOLAI RIMSKY-KORSAKOFF
(1844–1908)
arranged by Hywel Davies

THE GADFLY
Romance

DMITRI SHOSTAKOVICH
(1906-1975)
arranged by Hywel Davies

JAZZ SUITE No 2
Second waltz

DMITRI SHOSTAKOVICH
(1906-1975)
arranged by Hywel Davies

PIANO CONCERTO No 2
Theme from second movement

DMITRI SHOSTAKOVICH
(1906–1975)
arranged by Christopher Norton

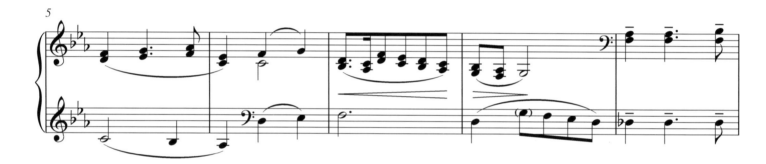

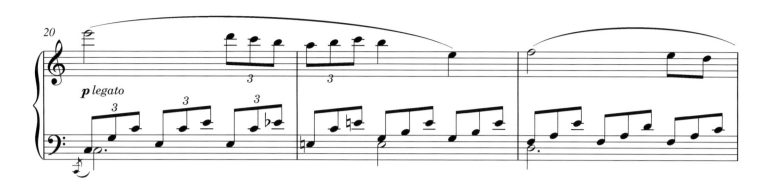

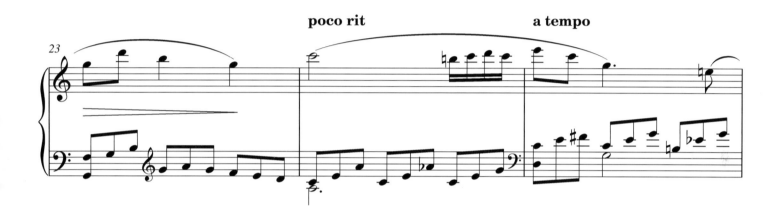

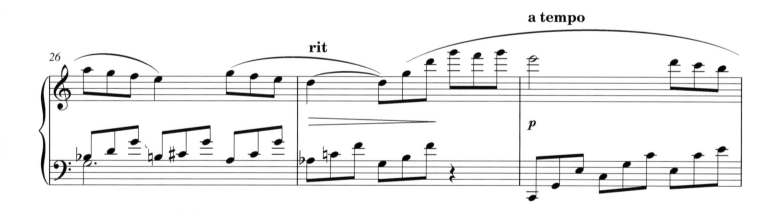

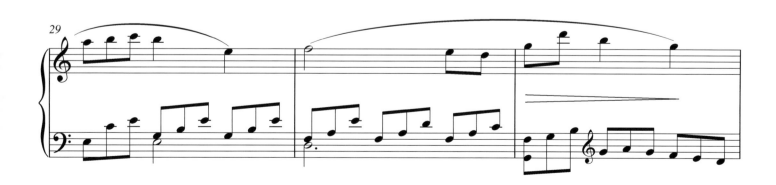

DC al Coda

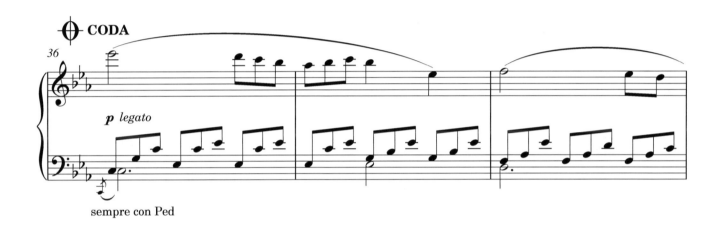

sempre con Ped

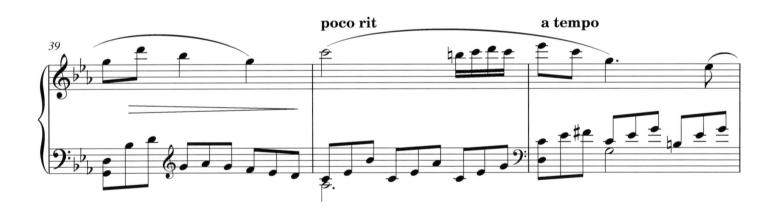

SYMPHONY No 5
Theme from second movement

DMITRI SHOSTAKOVICH
(1906–1975)
arranged by Christopher Norton

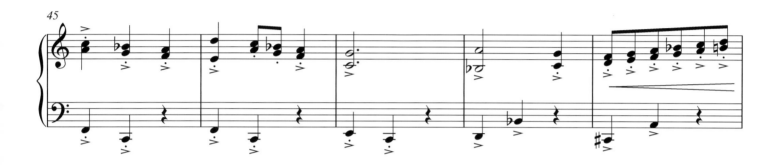

THE FAIRY'S KISS
Theme

IGOR STRAVINSKY
(1882–1971)
arranged by Christopher Norton

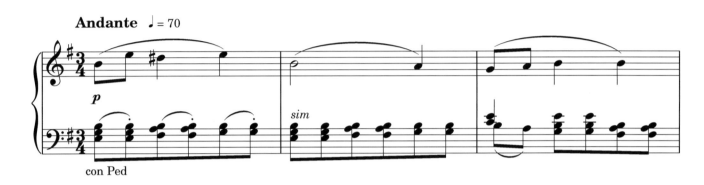

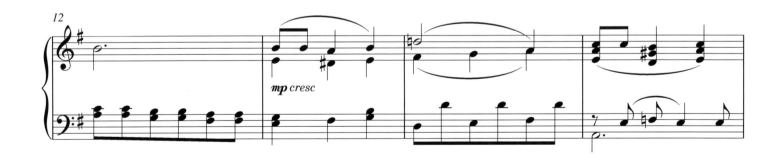

SYMPHONIES OF WIND INSTRUMENTS
Fragment

IGOR STRAVINSKY
(1882–1971)
piano reduction by Igor Stravinsky

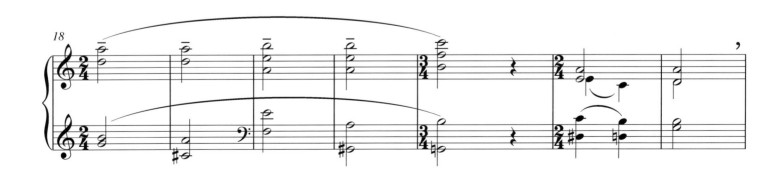

THE NUTCRACKER
Waltz of the flowers

PETER TCHAIKOVSKY
(1840–1893)
arranged by Hywel Davies

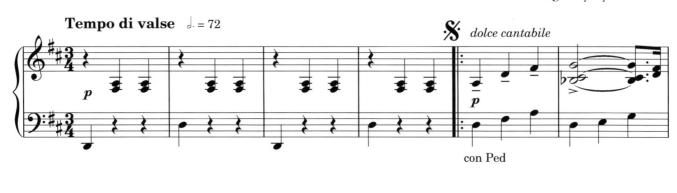

DS al Coda

SWAN LAKE
Scène (Act II)

PETER TCHAIKOVSKY
(1840–1893)
arranged by Hywel Davies

SYMPHONY No 5
Theme from second movement

PETER TCHAIKOVSKY
(1840–1893)
arranged by Hywel Davies